# My Feeling Better Workbook

## Activities That Help Kids Beat the Blues

By: Sarah W. Hamil, CMSW, RPT, ATR

My Feeling Better Workbook—Activities That Help Kids Beat the Blues
By Sarah W. Hamil, CMSW, RPT, ATR

Illustration & Design: Robin C. Morris

ISBN 1-931704-07-4

Published by:
Instant Help Books
4 Berkeley Street
Norwalk, CT 06850
203-838-9794
www.InstantHelpBooks.com

# Table of Contents

# Introduction

Dear Reader,

Everyone has times when they feel sad or "blue." It is natural to have sad and uncomfortable feelings when we are tired or lonely or disappointed. These feelings are just part of life.

Sometimes sad feelings become a regular thing, and we have *the blues*. This means we aren't just a little blue or a little sad from time to time, but we have sad feelings that just won't go away. When this happens, it is hard to be friendly, hard to do schoolwork, or hard to do chores at home. Sometimes it is even difficult to have fun and enjoy playing.

If feelings of sadness won't go away and make us feel yucky, it is time to take action. It is time to feel better and beat *the blues*!

- Sarah Hamil

# Facts About the Blues

- Both adults and children can get the blues.

- The blues can make us feel very tired, sad, and tearful.

- You didn't do anything wrong or bring the blues on yourself.

- The blues may be really bad one day and better the next day.

- Sometimes the blues are followed by lots of energy or feeling "hyper."

- The blues can cause us to forget to do important things at home and school.

- The blues can lead us to think nobody likes us and other bad thoughts.

- Sometimes a doctor says medicine is needed to help with the blues.

- You can feel better and beat the blues!

# Day After Day

Amy felt blue again today. She had thought that surely today would be different, but it was the same as before. Day after day, Amy was blue and she just couldn't think what to do. School was going okay; but most days it was hard to pay attention in class, and she was getting behind in her schoolwork.

At recess, she really didn't feel like playing and would wander alone in the playground. She would stare at the different colors in the grass and think to herself.

Alice was Amy's best friend. Now Alice was playing with Robert on the swings each day because Amy was not interested in talking or swinging. Amy really wished that Alice and Robert would come over to her and ask her to play, but her friends thought that Amy wanted to be left alone.

Day after day, Amy was blue and she just couldn't think what to do. The next day, Mom asked Amy if she wanted her friends to come over for an afternoon snack and to play. Amy thought this sounded like fun, but her answer to Mom was, "Whatever, I don't care." That afternoon went by, and Amy spent her time watching television by herself at home.

At supper that night, Mom asked Amy how she was feeling and Amy said, "Okay." Amy finished her supper and went to bed hoping that the next day would be better.

Day after day, Amy was blue and she just couldn't think what to do. It is time for Amy to feel better and beat the blues!

When the blues show up day after day and we can't think what to do, it is time to TAKE ACTION!

We will take action by talking about this blue feeling and trying some new things to beat the blues.

This workbook is designed to give you different activities that help you build the skills you need to feel better. These activities are meant to be fun and creative. The ones you really like can be repeated and changed as you come up with new ideas. Others you may try once and decide to move on to other activities. Let's get started!

## Day after Day...A Different Story

Amy felt better this morning. She woke up and started her daily basic self-care. She brushed her teeth, combed her hair, and put on her favorite shirt. She was ready for school!

Day after day, Amy had been blue; but now she was learning what to do!

School had been hard for a week or two, but now she was remembering to talk to her teacher when she felt lost or behind in her work. Amy's teacher had been a big help. At recess, she was spending time with Alice and Robert on the swings, and recently she had made new friends who liked to jump rope. Amy had never tried jumping rope until last week, and she found that this was one of her favorite things to do. All that jumping helped her to get moving and feel great.

Day after day, Amy had been blue; but now she was learning what to do!

Mom offered to have all of Amy's friends over for pizza and play time. Amy thought about it and said, "That's awesome! Let's do it tomorrow because I want to ride my bike this afternoon."

That afternoon, Amy finished her homework, rode her bike, and had a good supper. As she snuggled into bed, she felt excited and looked forward to tomorrow.

Day after day, Amy had been blue and now she knew what to do!

# How Blue Are You?

Take a few moments, and think about how often you feel sad or blue.

Do you feel sad or upset everyday, or is it just at certain times?

There are seven days in a week. How many days a week do you feel blue? _____

Do you feel bad most of the day or at certain times? _____

Write the time of day you feel the most blue: _____

Use a blue marker or crayon, and color the person on the next page in a way that shows how blue you feel.

# How Blue Are You?

Now use different colors to show feelings other than sadness.

Be sure to come up with a feeling that goes with the color. Remember, this is how you feel right now or how you have been feeling recently. Feelings change, and we will work on feeling better; but first we need to see what the feelings look like in this picture.

List all the colors used in the *How Blue Are You?* drawing.

Write the feeling you associate with the color. You may have several feelings with each color.

<u>Color</u>                     <u>Feelings</u>

_____       _____

_____       _____

_____       _____

_____       _____

_____       _____

_____       _____

_____       _____

Be sure to list the color blue.

We are using the phrase *the blues* as a way to describe feeling sad or down, but the color blue can have other meanings as well.

List all the other feelings you have for blue!

Talk to others about colors and feelings. People have lots of ideas about colors and also about how they feel. It is very important that you say how you feel when you are trying to beat the blues.

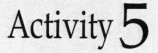

# Thought Check: Naming Our Thoughts

Let's do a thought check to see if you have some thoughts that are making you feel blue. We all have thoughts about ourselves. We may think we are smart, funny, or handsome. At times, we may have thoughts about ourselves that make us feel sad and tired of trying.

To feel better, it is necessary to identify sad thoughts that may be stuck in our heads.

What are your thoughts about how you feel right now?

_____

_____

_____

_____

_____

_____

_____

_____

_____

_____

_____

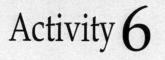

# Thought Check:
# Naming Our Thoughts

What do your thoughts look like?

Draw a face showing your thoughts and feelings right now.

Draw a face showing how you may look when you have sad thoughts.

# Thought Check: Naming Our Thoughts

Each of us has a name. When someone is looking for you, they call your name, and then you probably say: *"Here I am!"*

Since you are learning to look for thoughts that help you feel better, you are going to name your thoughts so that we can find a way to beat the blues.

The thoughts that make us feel better about ourselves are given the name **Positive Thoughts (or P+.)**

The thoughts that make us feel sad and tired of trying are given the name **Negative Thoughts (or N-.)**

Let's practice naming thoughts. Use the codes **P+** or **N-** to name these thoughts.

I like to spend time with my friends.       _____

Nobody likes me.       _____

I can't do anything right.       _____

I will try something new today.       _____

I did my best on this work.       _____

I'm always in trouble.       _____

I will ask for help with this problem.       _____

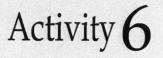
Write five thoughts of your own.

_____

_____

_____

_____

_____

Now look at the thoughts you have written, and label them as Positive (P+) or Negative (N-).

# Thought Check: Self-Talk Activity 7

The next thing we have to do to beat *the blues*, is to think about our thoughts!

This is kind of tricky because most of us think without being aware of all of our thoughts. We tell ourselves things in our head about how we feel about other people and how we think they feel about us.

Most important are the thoughts we think about ourselves. The words and stories that you keep in your mind are called "self-talk."

"Self-talk" is a fancy word for all that stuff you say to yourself in your mind about how you feel and how you understand what happens to you.

On the next page, write down everything that you are thinking *right now*. See if you can write for five minutes without stopping.

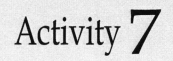

On the lines below, write exactly what you are thinking.  Or you can tell an adult what you are thinking, and he or she will write it.

_____

_____

_____

_____

_____

_____

_____

_____

_____

_____

_____

_____

_____

_____

_____

_____

_____

_____

_____

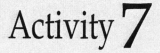

# Thinking About Thoughts and Self-Talk

Look at the picture below, and tell a story about it in your mind.

You are talking to yourself about this picture. What you are saying to yourself about the picture is self-talk.

Keep the talk in your head and try not to speak out loud about the picture just yet, because you are learning how to hear your self-talk.

What do you hear yourself saying about the picture?

Think to yourself about how you feel about this picture.

Tell yourself about these feelings.

Would you like to change the picture or add something to it?

Listen to your self-talk, and make the changes you hear!

You may draw other things you would like to see in the picture or add color as you would like.

# Thought Check: Listening to Self-Talk

This part of "Thought Check" will help you decide if your self-talk is helping you feel better or if your self-talk is making it hard for you to beat the blues.

Many things happen to us each day. Think of all the different experiences you have daily and during the week.

Put a check by the things you do often.

___Spend time with my family       ___Spend time with friends

___Play with others       ___Play by myself

___Go to school       ___Do other activities (for example, video games)

___Go to appointments (doctor, counselor)       ___Watch TV

___Play sports       ___Take care of myself/hygiene

___Spend time alone       ___Listen to music

___Do homework       ___Perform daily chores

List other ways you spend your time that are not listed above.

_____       _____

_____       _____

_____       _____

_____       _____

_____       _____

_____       _____

_____       _____

In the first two parts of the "Thought Check" activity, you learned to hear your self-talk expressions. Now it is important to listen to what you have to say about the things you do each week.

Take a few minutes to think about how you feel about the things you do daily and each week. Pay careful attention to what you say to yourself about these experiences. These are your self-talk statements about your life experiences!

Some of the things we do each day are really fun and make us feel good. Some of the things we do are hard work and require us to push ourselves.

Hard work is not a bad thing; but when we have the blues, we may feel like giving up on things. When we give up, we feel bad about ourselves and our thoughts, and self-talk becomes negative. When we feel good about our efforts and want to try again, our thoughts and self-talk become positive.

Using markers or crayons, pick a color that can be used to show good feelings and positive self-talk.

What is the color? (Use it here.)

Now pick a color that can be used to show uncomfortable feelings and negative self-talk.

What is the color? (Use it here.)

Also pick a color for things for which you have both positive and negative self-talk.

What is the color? (Use it here.)

# Thought Check:
# Listening to Self-Talk

Go to the checklist of things you do often on page 19. Listen to your self-talk, and do a thought check about all of the things you do each day or during the week.

Use the colors you have chosen to show your thoughts and self-talk for each experience.

• **Try to pick out exactly what helps you to feel good about the things you do.**

What helps you to have thoughts that make you feel good about yourself?

_____

_____

_____

_____

_____

_____

_____

# Activity 10

## That's Not True!

Now that you have learned to listen to your self-talk, let's look at how true your self-talk statements are.

We will look at some general statements we sometimes say to ourselves that just aren't true! First check out certain words that can let us know when we may be stretching the truth:

Everybody                    Always                    Never

These are called "absolute" words. Absolute words mean things are extreme or exaggerated. Most of the things we do are not extreme or exaggerated.

Read the statements below, and decide if they could be true. If the statements are hard to believe, you can say, "That's not true!"

I always play video games.

I never get to watch TV.

Everybody likes to play soccer.

I'm always last in line.

Everybody does math better than me.

I never miss a day of school.

I'm always first.

Everybody picks me last.

I'm always in trouble.

Cross out the absolute words in the statements above.

Now read them again without the absolute words and decide if they could be true.

After you take the absolute words out of the statements, think of a way they can be said using any words other than the absolute words.

# That's Not True!

Let's play with the absolute words. Finish these statements.

     I always _____.

     I never _____.

     Everybody _____.

Read the statements you have written, and decide if they are true.

Cross out the absolute words in your statements, and think of a way the statement can be said using any words other than the absolute words.

Which statements communicate your thoughts and feelings best?

Of course, there are times when we use absolute words to say just what we mean. There are other times when we do a thought check and listen to our self-talk and decide to say, "That's not true!"

Draw a picture of something that you really do *all* the time.

# That's Not True! Activity 10

Draw a picture of something that you *never* do.

Draw a picture of something that you *everybody* does.

# That's Not True!

Draw a picture of something that you do *sometimes*.

Draw a picture of something that *some* people do, but not everybody.

## Shape Your Day with Positive Thoughts

Everyone needs to hear encouraging words each day. It is nice to have others encourage us, but there are times when we can use our self-talk to remind ourselves of our possibilities and potentials.

When we have the blues, we may forget that we have lots of talents and good qualities. You can "shape your day" with a daily dose of encouragement.

Say the positive thoughts below out loud.

I will ask for help when I need support.

I am friendly and I like being with others.

I will try something new today.

I am a good person.

I will remember my strengths.

I am proud of myself.

I am awesome!

I am making progress every day.

I will talk about my feelings with a safe person.

The two best things about me are _____ and _____!

I will think of my favorite color today.

I will remember the kind things others have said to me.

Now say them to yourself.

I will ask for help when I need support.

I am friendly and I like being with others.

I will try something new today.

I am a good person.

I will remember my strengths.

I am proud of myself.

I am awesome!

I am making progress every day.

I will talk about my feelings with a safe person.

The two best things about me are _____ and _____!

I will think of my favorite color today.

I will remember the kind things others have said to me.

# Daily Dose

Write down five other positive thoughts.

1. _____

_____

2. _____

_____

3. _____

_____

4. _____

_____

5. _____

_____

Say them out loud, and then repeat them in your mind.

To feel better and beat the blues we need a plan. It is like going on a trip to visit someone. It is important to think about the direction you want to go and the things you will need to make your trip successful.

Where do we want to go? We will set a goal.

How are we going to get there? We will make a plan.

We will map it out!

For this activity, you need an adult to help look at a map. Any map is fine.

Find a map and look at all the roads, highways, lakes, rivers, and cities. Look at all the different ways to go and all the choices that are available. A map of any state would be fine.

Pick a city in the state and check out all the different ways there are to get to the city or to get out of the city.

Choose a starting point, and make a square to show where to start. Color it any color you like.

Now, using the map on the next page, take markers, pens, or crayons and create a path from the starting point one point to another. This is our plan:

Next choose the place you want to visit, your destination. Use a star shape to show where you will finish, and color it in any way you like.

Now, between the starting point and the destination there will be a route or a path that you will choose. Use a color you like to make a line along the route you have chosen. Finish the map by adding color or anything you think it needs.

# Map It Out:  Making a Plan

## Where Do You Want to Go?

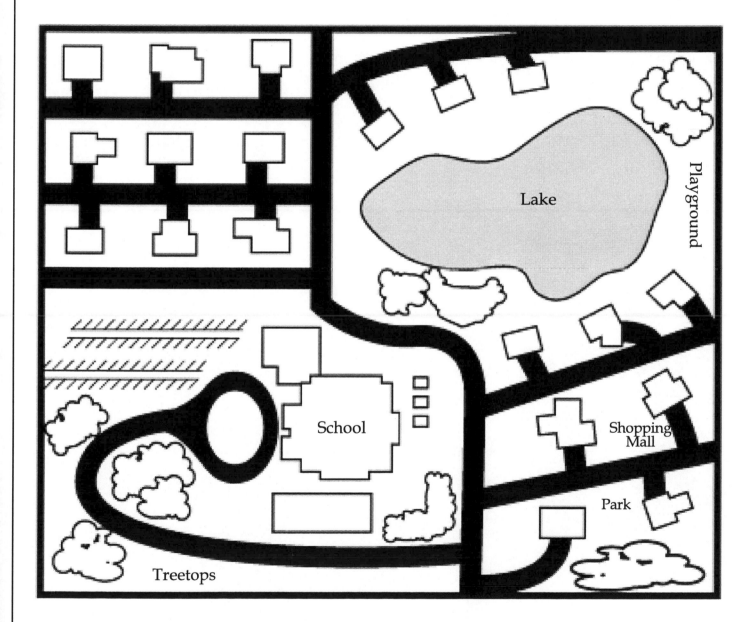

Mapping things out and setting goals for ourselves can be fun. Often when we have the blues, it is hard to get started on things, even things that we like to do and especially things we don't like to do.

### Getting Started

Imagine doing the activities listed below. Each of these things has a starting point. Next to each activity, write one thing you would need to do to get started or to begin the task.

Ride a bike to a friend's house.          _____

Solve a math problem.          _____

Make a new friend.          _____

Think of two things that you like to do, and write them in the spaces below.

1. _____

2. _____

Now write the first thing you do to begin each of the tasks you listed.

1. _____

2. _____

# Map It Out:  Getting Started and Moving Along

*Moving Along.*

After getting started, we find a way to move forward and reach our destination. There are usually many steps involved in any task.

*For Example.*

1. If you would like to make a new friend, the starting point is to say, "Hello."

2. Then you need to be friendly.

3. Next you might talk to that person about the things you both like to do.

4. After talking about things you both like to do, you could ask that person to play a game.

5. Finally you may invite him or her to your home or to sit with you at lunch. There are many steps to making friends after getting started. But it is worth the effort because friends are important to us.

*Your Move.*

1. In the example above, use a green marker to highlight the starting point in making a new friend.

2. Use a yellow marker to highlight the steps needed after the starting point.

3. Use any other color to circle the destination or the reason for saying hello.

Try to remember how you and your best friend first met.

1. What were you doing?

_____

2. Who said hello first?

_____

3. Write the names of your friends in the space below.

_____

Draw a picture of you and your best friend.

# Map It Out: Practice for Success

Let's practice mapping it out and moving along with the plan.

On the next page, make a drawing of someone building something that is interesting to you. If you prefer cut a picture from a magazine or newspaper and glue it here.

Give the picture you created a name. _____

What is the starting point for the task in the picture?

     Starting point: _____

List 2 or 3 simple steps needed to complete the task or to reach the pictured goal.

    1. _____

    2. _____

    3. _____

## Review

Let's review the steps to Map It Out.

Picture a task or something you need to do.

Identify the starting point.

List the steps needed to reach your goal.

Do the task and enjoy your success!

Now it is time to map out a plan to feel better and beat the blues. Here's the plan.

**Getting Started**

Review the goals on the next page. The goals are important skills that everyone needs to get along in life, and they are especially important when you are working to feel better and to beat the blues.

Choose a goal that is a skill you would like to develop or improve. This will be something that will help you right now.

**Moving Along**

The way to reach your goal is to use the workbook activities and practice your new skills. These new things will be interesting and fun to try.

**High Five!**

When you reach your goal, be sure to take time to be proud of yourself and tell yourself, "Way to go!" Get a friend or an adult to give you a high five.

**Keep Building Skills**

After reaching one goal, let's go for more. Set another goal and continue to build up your skills so that you will feel better and beat the blues.

**Put a check mark by the three goals that are most important to you.**

☐ **Build confidence**

Feel good about your abilities to make friends, play games, and try new things.

☐ **Be creative**

Express your personal style and true feelings with art, play, and music.

☐ **Improve self-control**

Have more control over your thoughts and behaviors.

☐ **Learn self-expression**

Learn about your feelings and how to talk about them.

☐ **Get moving**

Feel better by exercising your body.

☐ **Learn about identity**

Get to know yourself better.

☐ **Practice self-care**

Take care of yourself by learning more about good daily habits.

☐ **Improve communication**

Speak up about your thoughts and feelings.

☐ **Try new problem-solving skills**

Practice making good decisions, and find different ways of working things through successfully.

☐ **Establish boundaries**

Know how to set limits, and respect the rights of others.

It is exciting to set goals for ourselves and to get started on new projects. Let's practice being organized and putting the most important things first.

## Goal Planner

My goal:       I would really like to try_____

_____

OR

              I would like to learn how to _____

_____

Step 1:       The starting point is _____

_____

Step 2:       The work I will need to do includes_____

_____

_____

_____

Step 3 :      After I do the projects, I will be proud of myself because I have a new skill!

On the next page, draw a picture of how you look when you feel proud of yourself. Or you can paste in a photograph of yourself.

First Things First

## Basic Self-Care

As we grow, we learn how to take care of ourselves. Each day we do regular stuff like brush our teeth, take a bath or shower, get dressed, play, and eat meals. These things may seem simple, but they are really important. Sometimes the blues cause us to neglect daily self-care. You are special, and this means that you need to take special care of yourself each day. Basic self-care is all that stuff you just have to do everyday to stay healthy.

## Dog Days!

Let's think about self-care by looking at what animals need each day to stay healthy.

For example, a puppy depends upon the mother to clean, feed, and protect him. Then as the puppy grows he learns to do these things for himself as well as many other things that make for happy and healthy dog days!

Here is a list of basic care the puppy needs.

| | |
|---|---|
| Rest | Take a bath |
| Play | Hang around others |
| Eat meals | Have protection |
| Find food | Learn tricks |

1. Use a green marker to put a dot by the things the puppy can do for himself.

2. Use a yellow marker for the care for which the puppy needs just a little help.

3. Use a purple marker to show the things the puppy depends on others to do for him.

As the puppy grows, there will be more and more things he can do for himself, but he will always need a little help with some things from people or other dogs.

What is your favorite animal? _____

Think of a time when you have watched this animal. Maybe your favorite animal is your family pet or one you have seen in the zoo or read about in books.

Draw a picture of your favorite animal doing something, or find a picture you like that shows an animal doing something.

1.  What is the animal doing in the picture?

2.  What does this animal need each day to stay healthy?

3.  Can this animal do these things alone or is help needed?

4.  How does the animal communicate what it needs?

5.  What might happen if the animal didn't have the basics? People and animals have a lot
    in common. They each need to be cared for every day. Basic self-care is important, so
    don't miss a day!

# Back to Basics: Part One

Here is a list of the daily basics. Beside each of the basics, identify a new and interesting way to complete the task.

Get out of bed _____

Brush teeth _____

Take a bath or shower _____

Get dressed _____

Brush or comb hair _____

Eat healthy meals _____

Rest _____

Take care of bedroom _____

Walk, run, or skip (exercise) _____

Play _____

Take medicine if needed _____

Spend time with family _____

Spend time with friends _____

Spend personal time _____

Go to bed _____

Which of these basics are easy for you to do?

_____

Which of these basics are boring?

_____

Which of these basics do you avoid or try to forget?

_____

# Back to Basics: Part Two

Try this! Often, we do the things we like to do first and then don't get around to doing those things we don't like. Try doing your least favorite "basics" first; then move on to your fun and easy favorites.

Another hint: For the things that you don't like, try doing them in a different way. For example, if brushing your teeth is a drag, hop on one foot while brushing your front teeth and hop on the other for the back teeth. You get the idea.

Take care of the basics everyday to feel better and beat the blues.

Did you do your basics today?

## Basic Self-Care Daily Worksheet

Some of our basics we do without being reminded, and that is great! Use this form as a checklist for the basics that you may forget.

### Basic Self-Care Tasks

In the morning …

_____

_____

_____

_____

In the afternoon …

_____

_____

_____

_____

Before bedtime …

_____

_____

_____

_____

Take care of your basics every day to feel better and beat the blues!

## Basic Training

Basic training is the phrase used by people in the military to describe the time they spend preparing their bodies and minds for battle. This is a time of hard work, but when basic training is finished the person feels strong and prepared.

Let's have our own basic training to feel better and beat the blues.

**Basic Training Goal**

Be active, and plan a time to walk, run, skip, or dance every day.

## Coaching Yourself

We want to train our minds and bodies to help us feel better, so it is time to learn how to be a coach. A coach is someone who wants us to be the best. It is the coach's job to give us some support and guidance when we feel like giving up. We discussed self-talk in the "thought check" section of the workbook. Now it is time to practice new self-talk or coaching self-talk. Coaching self-talk gets us moving and encourages us to get the job done.

Here are some of the things we need to say to ourselves with coaching self-talk.

| | |
|---|---|
| I can do this. | I'm doing great. |
| Let's get started. | Get moving. |
| Good job. | Keep trying. |
| Way to go! | Keep going. |

Put a circle around the phrases above that you will use to coach yourself in basic training.

Our bodies help us cope with stress and tension, so we want our body to be strong and healthy. To be at our best, we need to get moving and be active!

What is your action style?

Think about how you feel about being active. Read these three activity styles, and pick your type. Put a circle around the action style that is like you.

1. Slow to go
This type of person finds it hard to get moving and would rather not be active.

2. On the go
This type of person will like getting going and likes to be active.

3. Busy bee
This type of person is almost constantly moving and has a hard time being still.

Now it is time to match your style with your goal.

Goals for each action style:

Slow to go ...................... Goal: Get moving and be active.

On the go ............ Goal: Stay active and try new things.

Busy bee......................... Goal: Stay active and pace yourself.

Circle the goal above that you think is most important to you.

Now for a different way of being active, try the "My Move" activity on the next page.

Don't forget to use coaching self-talk!

This is a new twist on exercise. Try this:

Think about what type of movement you like the best.

| | |
|---|---|
| Hopping | Twisting |
| Walking | Jogging |
| Skipping | Stepping |
| Dancing | Swaying |
| Wiggling | Marching |
| Running | Jumping |

Get up and do the movement you like.

Next, add your personal style to this movement by...

| | |
|---|---|
| Clapping | Snapping your fingers |
| Making a funny expression | Singing |

Now you can say, "This is My Move."

Ask a friend or someone in your family to join in the game. Allow the other person to show their favorite movement. *Watch closely and copy the movement.*

Take turns making up new movements and trying to remember each person's move. Mix it up by adding different moves. All of a sudden, you have a whole routine or a dance going!

**In a Group**
This activity can be great with 4 to 6 people. Have each person say their name and demonstrate a movement. Can you remember what the first person's move was?

As a name is called, everyone in the group makes that person's move.

# Big Steps, Small Steps

Take a look at your feet.

Our feet allow us to move in all directions, and they allow us to take the steps we need to reach our goals. Since we are learning new ways to work on things, let's be creative while thinking about the steps we are going to take to feel better and beat the blues.

These feet are going to be busy making progress; so give the feet below some color and style by using markers, pencils, or crayons to make them unique.

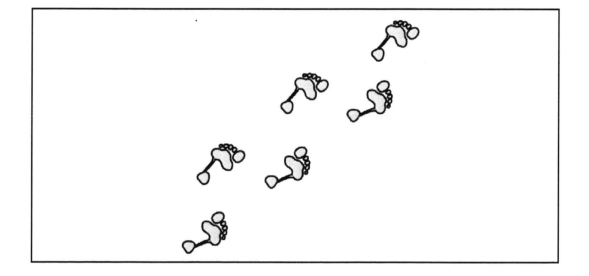

# Activity 20

# Big Steps, Small Steps

Some steps are easy to take, and we call these *small steps*.

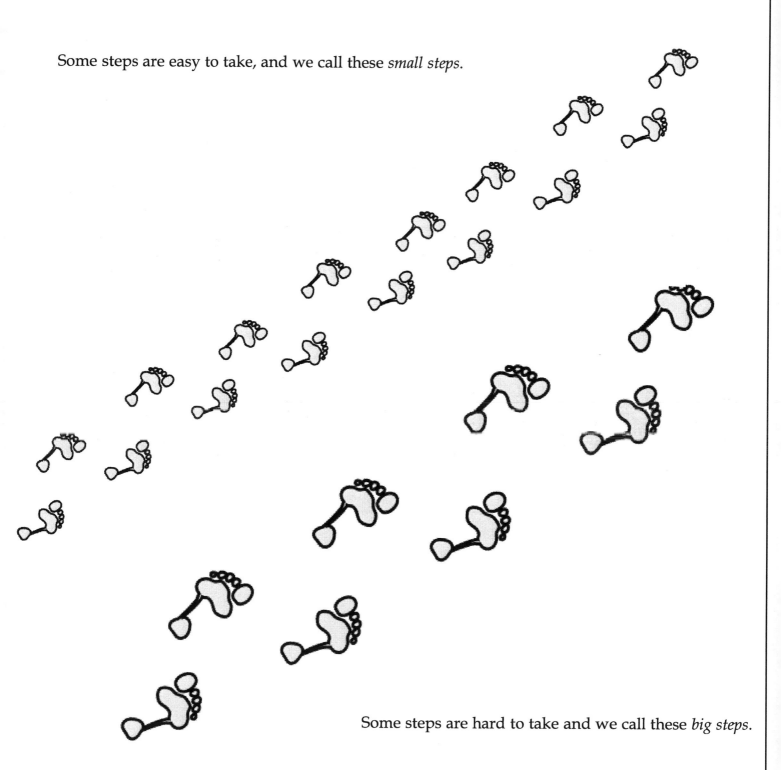

Some steps are hard to take and we call these *big steps*.

# Big Steps, Small Steps

When trying to feel better and beat the blues, we talk a lot about taking steps to reach our goals. We have already learned how to set goals and a way to list the steps to the goal.

Now we will talk about the type of steps we will be taking, because steps are different for each goal we set. We have talked about many different goals for feeling better about ourselves.

On the next page, let's review our goals and what each of them means.

**Build confidence**

Feel good about your abilities to make friends, play games, and try new things.

**Be creative**

Express your personal style and true feelings with art, play, and music.

**Improve self-control**

Have more control over your thoughts and actions.

**Learn self-expression**

Learn about your feelings and how to talk about them.

**Get moving**

Feel better being active and exercising your body every day.

**Learn about identity**

Get to know yourself better.

**Practice self-care**

Take care of yourself by learning good daily habits.

**Improve communication**

Speak up about your thoughts and feelings.

**Try new problem-solving skills**

Practice making good decisions, and find different ways of working things through successfully.

**Establish boundaries**

Know how to set limits, and respect the rights of others.

# Big Steps, Small Steps

You already have many skills that help you do the things that must be done each day. Some of the things you make an effort to do are easy and some are hard.

You probably already have reached some of the goals listed, and these will just be a review for you.

After looking over the goals, decide which of them will be *big steps* for you and which ones will be *small steps*. Put a check mark by the goals you feel like you have already worked through.

Put a colorful circle by the goals that you think will take *small steps* to complete.

Put a star by the goals that will be a *big step* in beating the blues.

Decide what goal would be best for you to start with, and let's get to work!

Remember that all the steps we take are important, both the big steps and small steps. Look through the workbook activities, and select one that looks like fun and that will help you reach your goal.

Go ahead and try to do something that is a big step for you. You may be surprised by your abilities!

Some days, all the things we need to do feel like a big effort, and we feel like giving up. We may say something like "Just forget it" or "What is the point of doing this?"

In this small box, draw the face of a person who feels like giving up on things.

# Make a Path

When we have the blues, this type of feeling gets in the way of feeling better.

We will get this feeling out of the way by making a path to beat the blues.

For this activity, you will need 4 different objects and 2 small pieces of paper.

On one piece of paper, write START and on the other write FINISH.

Find 4 small objects, such as stuffed animals, empty boxes, or balls.

This activity is great to do outside, where you can move around; but if necessary you can be inside.

**Part One**

Put the START piece of paper in a location to be the beginning of your path. Make a winding path and place the FINISH paper at the point you decide is the end. For example if you are in your room, you will walk in a wide circle and then cut back in a zigzag to reach your finish.

Walk along the path you have created. Try to remember the first pattern you created to walk along, beginning at start and ending at finish.

**Part Two**

Now take the four objects you collected, and put them in different places along your path. These are your obstacles, or the things that will get in your way between START and FINISH. If you are the type of person who has a hard time getting things started, put one of the obstacles at the starting point.

Once again you will walk along the path you have created; but when you get to the obstacle, you will decide how to get around or deal with this problem.

There are several choices to make along the path.

Do you want to just walk around the obstacles?

Maybe you want to pick them up and carry them to the finish.

Perhaps you will hop over them

Be creative with your choices, and find a path to make your way along the route from start to finish.

When you are having a hard time meeting your goals, what type of things get in your way?

List them here: _____

_____

_____

_____

_____

_____

_____

_____

What choices would help you get around these obstacles?

List them here: _____

_____

_____

_____

_____

_____

_____

_____

# Flying Feathers

Staying active and playing require getting started, taking the steps needed, and using self-control. Self-control means using our mind to guide our actions. For example, it takes self-control to hop on one foot. Our mind has to tell our body to hold one foot up while we hop on the other. Then our mind and body work together to figure out where we hop and how long we hop.

These are other examples of self-control.

Staying seated at school         Playing catch with a friend

Listening to others              Talking to others

Think of three things you do that require you to use self-control and write them here.

1. _____

2. _____

3. _____

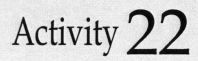

Sometimes it is hard to have self-control. For example, it is easy to forget to wait our turn when playing a game, because we are excited and want to be part of the action.

Each day there are situations in which we have to use self-control. Having self-control is easier when we practice self-talk and the coaching self-talk we discussed before.

Self-control statements would go like this:

|  |  |  |
|---|---|---|
| I need to slow down. | I will keep trying. | I am next. |
| I am learning to wait. | Just a few more minutes. | Here I go! |

Practice thinking the self-control statements while playing flying feathers.

# Flying Feathers

## The Flying Feathers Game

**What you need to play:** One regular plastic drinking straw, one small lightweight feather.

**Directions**: Place about one half of the feather in the end on the straw. Take a deep breath and BLOW! The feather will fly out of the end of the straw.

Can you keep it flying by blowing through the straw?

One thing to notice about the feather is that it is very hard to control. It takes lots of concentration and blowing to keep the feather going.

**Bonus!**
One of the bonuses of this activity is all that blowing. Slow deep breathing and blowing out is good for us and helps us feel better when we are tense. Remember the next time you feel tired or angry … BREATHE!

Think of a time when you would like to have more self-control.

Think of a time when you would like to be more relaxed and less tense.

Imagine using self-control statements and taking deep breaths at those times.

You can do it!

Newspapers are full of information that tells us what is going on in the world. This is a newspaper devoted entirely to you, so put your name in the title and let others know what is going on in your world.

## Make the Headlines

The headlines of the newspaper go on the front page, since they describe the most important things happening in your life right now.

Usually the front page story of the newspaper has a big picture to go along with the story. Draw something you like to go with the headlines, or add a picture you find in a magazine or your local newspaper.

## Inside Stories

• Report other daily news including stories about your friends and family.

• Don't forget to include pictures or stories describing your special interests.

Each day is a little different from the day before. Some days are exciting, and others are kind of dull. Some days are a combination of things we really like and things we would rather not do.

How was your day? Have you shared with another person what is going on with you ? It is very important that we find a way to let others know what is going on in our life.

Thanks for sharing *The Daily News*!

# My Daily News

## About Me
## My Family
## My Friends

Draw or place
photo here.

# My Daily News

Draw or place photo here.

# My Daily News

Draw or place photo here.

Draw or
place
photo here.

# My Daily News

Draw or place
photo here.

# Open Mike

It is time to practice our communication skills. Communication happens when we share our thoughts with others and then listen to what the other person has to say to us.

Write the names of your family members in the space below.

_____          _____

_____          _____

_____          _____

Identify something that each family member does really well. Imagine they have become famous for this and are a big star because of their talent. It is your job to interview them for a special report.

Now we will play the Open Mike game with this person.
Use any material you have available—such as paper and tape, clay, or play dough—to create a microphone. Use a toy or real microphone if you have one.

Open Mike means that the microphone ("mike") is "open" for communication.
Imagine that you are a TV reporter for the evening news and your family member is famous for their skill! You can say anything you want.

Use your microphone to start the interview. Try to really act the part of a reporter, and encourage the other person to pretend they are a celebrity or big star.

Is it easy for you to speak up to others about your thoughts and feelings?

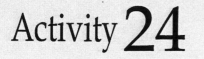

**Open Mike Interview Guide**

Hello!  My name is _____ and I am here tonight with an amazing story

about _____ (family member's name).

We have just learned that _____ is famous for the outstanding ability to

_____.

I am very interested in what you have to say.  Please tell me all about yourself.


Listen carefully to what the person has to say, and continue to ask questions to learn as much as you can about the other person.

After the interview ask the other person to interview you about your special skills.

# Create a Monster

All of us have times when we feel afraid. Fear is a strong feeling, and we expect to feel afraid when we are in danger. But sometimes we feel scared because we have the blues and our thoughts are sad and scary.

When we have the blues, we may create a monster in our mind! We are going to call this Monster Thinking.

Monster Thinking happens when we have the same scary thoughts over and over, even when we know everything is okay. For example, there are times when we are afraid of the dark. We turn on the light and see that everything is great, so we turn off the light. But the next thing you know, we are in the dark and we have created a monster in our mind.

## Help for Monster Thinking

In this activity, you will learn to:

- Look at your fears

- Talk to a person you trust about your fears

- Learn what makes you feel safe

We will start by looking at your fears. List the things that make you feel afraid.

_____

_____

_____

List your ideas about monsters or fears.

_____

_____

_____

What does your face look like when you are scared?

_____

_____

_____

# Create a Monster

Draw a scary face in the box below.

This activity will help you take charge over your fears.

We often create a monster in our mind when we feel sad and afraid.

What could this monster look like?

_____

_____

_____

Ask an adult to help you gather materials to create a monster.

Try to find materials, such as paper, play dough, clay, glue, sticks, pipe cleaners, or boxes. Use your imagination and create a monster. Play around with the materials and make your monster special by adding color, yarn, buttons, or glitter.

# Create a Monster

Tell a story about the monster.

Begin by saying, "Once upon a time there was a monster ... "

In the story below tell where the monster lives and who has power over the monster. Write the story.

_____

_____

_____

_____

_____

_____

_____

_____

_____

_____

REMEMBER

You will have power over the monster because you created it!

Creating a monster is one way of looking at your fears. Telling the story about the monster is a way of talking to others about fears.

## Feeling Safe and Protected

Each of us has our own idea of what makes us feel better when we are sad and scared.

In the space below, name the people and things that provide safety and comfort for you.

_____

_____

_____

Name three people with whom you feel comfortable talking about your fears.

1._____

2._____

3._____

Share your fears, and let others help you feel better.

# Create a Monster

Draw a safe place in the space below.

# Activity 26                                   My Self-Label

You have seen labels in clothes, on food, and on toys.

Many kids are familiar with labels and brands of toys, food, and clothes.

Labels explain what the item is, what it does, and what is inside.

Usually, a label is designed to catch your eye and make you interested in the item.

Find something that has a label.

What does the label say, and what does it look like?

Make a copy of the label here.

Does the label do a good job of describing this item?

Can you tell what the item is just by looking at the label?

Would you change the label? Make any changes you would like in the drawing.

## My Self-Label

Let's use the label idea to describe ourselves in a catchy and creative way.

This label is good only for today because we grow and change every day.

The self-label will include:

Who I am

What I like to do

What is inside or how I feel

Use the space below to make a self-label.

Since people don't come with labels, it is important that we find a way to let others know what we are really like. We can practice communicating the things we like, what our interests are, and how we truly feel on the inside.

*A word of caution: Some people may "label" others or think they know what a person is really like without taking time to get to know them. It is a good habit to describe ourselves and our own feelings and to avoid labeling others.

# Activity 27    Watching for Warning Signs

Some things come with warning labels that give very important information about special care needed to prevent an accident from happening. Warning labels inform about danger and keep people from getting hurt.

Warning labels even come on toys! You have seen them. They bring your attention to how the toy should be used and what age a person should be to play with the toy.

What is your favorite toy?

Did you read the instructions label on the toy or was there a warning?

What age should a person be to play with this toy?

Does your toy need special care, or is there a certain way to play with it?

Is there any way the toy could be harmful?

Even toys need special care. When you are letting a friend play with your toys, you give them the basic instructions on how to play and how the toys need to be treated.

When we have the blues, it is important for us to give others information about the special care needed to feel better. There are times when we are having a hard time with the little things during the day. The blues can make us feel tired and sad. This is a warning sign, and we need to let others know that we are struggling with the little things so they can help us stay on track. Some feelings are warning signs, and we can learn to recognize these feelings when they first come up.

Read the story "Ouch. That Hurts!" See if you can pick out the warning signs.

## "Ouch! That Hurts!"

One day Megan got out of bed and felt sleepy and tired. She wondered why she was tired after sleeping all night. Oh well, it was time to get ready for school, so she pushed ahead with brushing her teeth, combing her hair, and getting dressed. Megan was frustrated trying to find something to wear because none of her clothes seemed to match or feel right.

When Megan put on her pants, her finger was caught in the zipper. Megan thought, "Ouch! That hurts!" Then at breakfast Mom said, "Hurry up, or you will be late." Megan tried to eat her cereal quickly and bit her lip because she was chewing so fast. Megan said, "Ouch! That hurts!" Mom said, "Move it along, we have to go."

Megan hopped out of the chair and rushed to get her backpack. In her rush, she hit her leg on the chair and she said, "Ouch! That hurts!" Mom said, "Let's go right now."

Megan got in the car and rode with her mother to school. Neither Megan nor her Mom said anything on the way to school.

Now Megan was feeling really sad and tired. Megan went into school and made her way to her classroom. In the hall, her friend Devin ran up to say hello. Devin was moving fast and accidentally bumped into Megan and knocked her down. Megan wanted to say, "Ouch! That hurts!"; but she couldn't because she was crying. Devin said, "What's wrong with you? That was an accident and I'm sorry."

The teacher came over and asked Megan to get up and to stop that crying. The teacher reminded Megan that she had a lot of work to do today and it was time to get started with schoolwork.

# Watching for Warning Signs

**Warning Signs**

What was the first warning sign for Megan?

_____

Whom could she have told about her feelings?

_____

What could she have said to her Mom?

_____

What could Mom have said or done to help Megan?

_____

What can Megan say or do to work things out with Devin?

_____

How can Megan get help from her teacher?

_____

What feelings do you have that are warning signs for you?

_____

Whom can you talk to about these feelings?

_____

What helps you feel better?

_____

Did you notice that Megan is a very brave girl who was trying to take the steps to get her day started off on the right track? She just needed some support, and she missed the warning signs that she needed to ask for help from others.

Pay attention to those warning signs, and let others know you need some support!

Ever notice how you can feel real blue at certain times and then you feel better? Often there are situations that cause us to feel tense or stressed.

## Stressful Situations

Situations are places we go, things we do, or people we are around. Each day is made up of many different situations. Usually we are fine in our daily situations, but occasionally there are places, things, or certain people that leave us feeling tense and irritable. The word for those situations that make us feel tense is *stress*. There are times when we have stressful situations and we feel upset. That is when we need to find a way to talk about how we are feeling.

The following describes a game to practice talking about how you feel when you have been in a stressful situation, and to notice how feelings change when stress is removed.

Ask an adult to play the Freeze Up, Warm -Up game.

All you need to play the game is a paper towel and a glass of ice water. Imagine that the ice water is tension or stress.

Place your finger in the ice water until it gets cold. This takes about 30 seconds. Then remove it from the water.

Now think of as many words as possible to describe how your finger feels.

Of course, it is cold. But what other words can you think of to describe how this feels?

Does it take long for your finger to warm up?

Just as happens to the cold finger, our feelings can change when we get out of the stressful situation and talk about what is going on with us.

# Freeze Up, Warm Up

Identify your stressful situations.

Under each of these topics, write the places, things, or people that make you feel tense or irritable.

| Places | Things | People |
| --- | --- | --- |
| _____ | _____ | _____ |
| _____ | _____ | _____ |
| _____ | _____ | _____ |
| _____ | _____ | _____ |
| _____ | _____ | _____ |
| _____ | _____ | _____ |
| _____ | _____ | _____ |
| _____ | _____ | _____ |

Identify the things that help you warm up, or feel better.

Under each of the topics, write the places, things, or people that make you feel calm and at ease.

Places                          Things                          People

_____        _____        _____

_____        _____        _____

_____        _____        _____

_____        _____        _____

_____        _____        _____

_____        _____        _____

_____        _____        _____

_____        _____        _____

The next time you are faced with a stressful situation remember that, just like the finger, you will warm up when you are away from the stress (the ice water). Also, you will feel better faster if you remember to talk with someone about how you feel.

# It's a Mystery to Me

At times, we have feelings that are mysterious or hard to identify. We know they are there because we feel weird, but it is just hard to say exactly what the feeling is. Sometimes a feeling is hidden, or we cover it up with another feeling to avoid awkward situations.

We can find our hidden feelings, identify them, and talk about them so we can feel better and beat the blues.

Let's play a game to demonstrate how things that are hidden or covered up are harder to identify.

This game is called "It's a Mystery to Me."

What you need:

- 4 to 6 small brown paper sacks

- 4 to 6 interesting nonbreakable objects that can be hidden in the sacks

- Tape for the top of each bag

You or another person will collect objects to be hidden in the paper sacks.

When it is your turn to hide the objects, put them in the bag and tape the top shut. Hand the bag to the other person and let them try to identify what is inside by feeling the object inside the bag.

Give the person several chances to say what the item inside feels like.

Notice how something may feel familiar but it is still hard to identify because it is hidden or covered up. If you just can't be sure what an item is after feeling it, you say, "It's a mystery to me!" To identify what is being felt inside the bag, either look inside or ask for help.

# It's a Mystery to Me

Search the list below for feelings that are hard for you to recognize or identify. Put a check mark by the feelings that are a mystery to you.

| | | | | |
|---|---|---|---|---|
| Caring | Love | Sadness | Joy | Anger |
| Confusion | Happiness | Concern | Hurt | Silliness |
| Hopeful | Fear | Friendly | Nervous | Guilty |
| Frustration | Tired | Lonely | Energetic | Needy |

Search the list of feelings again for the feelings that you would rather hide. Put a circle around the feelings that you hide.

Sometimes we have to work hard to find feelings that are hidden. When you recognize you have hidden feelings, find a person you like and trust to talk with about your hidden feelings.

Look at the outline of a person on the next page.

Think about the feelings you checked and circled in the "It's a Mystery to Me" activity.

Where do you have these feelings in your body?

For example, when you feel tired, what part of your body feels this the most?

On the right side of the page, write 2 feelings that are a mystery to you.

On the other side of the page, write 2 feelings that you often hide from others.

Give each of these feelings a color.

Use the feeling colors on the person outline to show where you have each of these feelings in your body.

Draw a face. Does the person's face show how they are feeling?

Now that you know where you have these feelings in your body, you can listen to your body talk. Often we may have a headache or stomachache when we are hiding a feeling. When we realize our body is talking to us, we can get those feelings out and feel better fast.

# Activity 31

Have you ever lost something?  Surely that you have.

What did you lose? _____

Were you able to find it? _____

How did you feel? _____

Tell another person the story of how you lost something and how it was found.

_____

_____

_____

_____

_____

_____

_____

_____

_____

_____

_____

_____

_____

_____

_____

_____

_____

_____

_____

# Lost & Found

Draw a picture of something that you have lost.

When something, is lost we have a terrible feeling. We look everywhere we can think of for what is lost. Usually we get as many people as possible to help us look for what we are missing. When we are not able to find what was lost, we have a hard time accepting the loss and we may continue looking for days, weeks, or even months. This is a very sad feeling, and it takes time to feel better after a loss. Often we are able to find what we thought was lost, and this feeling is wonderful. We are relieved and very happy.

The blues can make us feel like we have lost our ability to speak up about how we feel. We will find our voices and speak up about how we feel. Get others involved as you work to feel better and beat the blues.

# Find the Words

Finding the right words to describe our feelings can be hard. Usually when we are asked, "How are you?" we answer, "I am fine."

When someone who cares about us asks us how we are, it is a good idea to find the words to let them know how we really feel.

Let's play a game called "Find the Words" to show how we feel.

What you need:

- 10 to 20 index cards or sheets of paper
- Markers, pens, or pencils

Write one feeling word on each index card.

Here is a list. You can add your own feeling words that are not listed here.

| | | | |
|---|---|---|---|
| Excited | Sad | Happy | Tired |
| Lonely | Friendly | Tense | Calm |
| Irritated | Silly | Interested | Lucky |
| Loving | Ignored | Frustrated | Hopeful |
| Curious | Overwhelmed | Guilty | Satisfied |

Add your own feeling words.

_____    _____    _____    _____

_____    _____    _____    _____

Ask an adult to play this game with you. The adult will hide the cards around the room.

After the feeling cards are hidden, it is your turn to "Find the Words" for how you feel.

As you find a card, read the feeling and decide whether that is how you feel right now. If that card is not the right word for you, keep searching until you find all the words to describe how you feel.

This activity will help you learn how to state clearly how you feel.

There are times when we need to let others know that we need their attention so we may be heard and understood.

When we have the blues, we may avoid speaking up about our true feelings; then we may feel lonely or ignored by others. But people around us can't read our minds or know how we really feel unless we let them know in a clear and direct way.

First, let's talk about the most important times for us to speak up.

- When we are hurt.
- When we are in danger.
- When another person is in danger.
- When we are confused or feel lost.
- When we have the bad feelings that bother us for a long time.

# Hey, Listen Up!

Let's practice speaking up about how we feel. For this activity all you need is the cardboard center part of a paper towel roll. This will be like a megaphone, which is an instrument that makes your voice heard.

Hold the megaphone (cardboard tube) up to your mouth and say...

Hey listen up! I am feeling _____

_____

_____

_____

_____

_____

_____

_____

Don't worry if you laugh or feel awkward at first. Keep practicing until you feel confident and until you have stated your feelings in a clear and direct way.

# My Favorites

Each of us has likes and dislikes.  We have people, places, and things that we prefer.

You are a very special person, and your thoughts and opinions matter.

When we feel blue, it is important to remember the things that make us feel comfortable.

Our favorite person to talk to or our favorite pillow when resting can be just what we need to feel better.

In the space below, identify your favorites.

My favorite people are:     _____

_____

_____

My favorite places are:     _____

_____

_____

My favorite things are:     _____

_____

_____

Think about the qualities of your favorites. What is it that makes them special to you?

Take time to enjoy your favorites and share your ideas about your favorites with another person. Ask another person to share their favorites with you.

Compare likes and dislikes with others. Keep an open mind, and maybe you will find another favorite!

# Strange Birds

Let's talk about those times when we feel strange. Feeling strange is to be expected when we are in stressful situations or when we are tense.

We will learn new ways to tolerate feeling strange until the feeling passes.

This activity is a relaxing and fun way to express what it is like to feel strange, and at the same time we can learn how to let that feeling pass.

Use the "Strange Bird" form on the next page, or use any art materials you have available to create a Strange Bird.

Be playful and creative making an image that looks strange.

After you have created your strange bird, come up with 5 to 10 words that describe it. Write the words below.

_____          _____

_____          _____

_____          _____

_____          _____

_____          _____

Here are a few examples of words that describe things that are strange.

| Weird | Cool | Wild | Different |
|-------|------|------|-----------|
| Foreign | Bizarre | Alien | Free-spirited |

Did you notice that when we found the words to describe the Strange Birds they are not so strange anymore!

# Activity 35

Complete this statement:  I feel like a Strange Bird when

_____

_____

_____

_____

_____

_____

_____

_____

_____

_____

_____

When you feel a little strange, think back on this Strange Bird and the words you used to describe it.  In a short time, that strange feeling will have passed and you will feel better.

# Activity 36      Signals: Stop, Slow, and Go

There are limits needed for the things we do each day. There are limits set for us by others, and there are limits we set for ourselves. In this activity, we will talk about how to communicate our limits to others so that we will feel safe and comfortable when we are around other people.

We use the word *boundary* to mean a line or a limit. For example, if you have a fence in your yard for your dog, this fence is the boundary for the dog. The fence limits the distance the dog can go. The fence or boundary also keeps some things inside and some things outside.

Use a pen, pencil, or marker to establish boundaries for each of the objects below. Decide whether some of the objects are inside a boundary together or each of them will be separated by the limits you set. Perhaps some of the boundaries will have gates that can be used as access.

Use a broken line to indicate a weak boundary that can be crossed.

Our personal boundaries are the limits we set for ourselves and for others.

We need to set personal boundaries that make us feel at ease when we are talking or playing with others.

The first step in setting your personal boundaries is to figure out the limits you are comfortable with for relating to others.

- Ask an adult to help you practice boundaries.

- The adult stands two giant steps away from you.

- How does this feel to you? Are you close enough to have a conversation?

- Now stand 1 arm's length away from the adult.

- How does this feel? What is it like to talk to someone at an arm's length?

- With close friends and family, we may sit side by side or hold hands, but that is because we know these people very well and we don't mind being up close.

What is your comfort zone, or the distance you like best, when you are with other people?

    2 Giant steps        1 Arm's length        Up close

Get to know your comfort zone in different situations, and practice letting others know your limits or boundaries.

Think about these situations, and pick your comfort zone.

    2 Giant steps        1 Arm's length        Up close

Playing with friends    _____

Talking to your family    _____

Meeting a new person    _____

We can give signals to others that communicate our personal boundaries.

The stop signal would be for:

>       People whom we want to keep at a distance

>       People we do not know or strangers

>       People we do not feel comfortable around

>       Someone we just met for the first time

The slow signal would be for those people we want to interact with in our comfort zone at an appropriate distance. Slow signals include shaking hands with people and giving someone a pat on the back. The slow signal would be for:

>       Friends whom we know and like

>       Some family members

>       People we are associated with at school

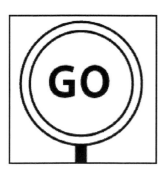

The go signal would be for close family and long-time friends. These are people whom we like to give us a hug or hold our hand. The go signal would be for:

>       People we know very well

>       Family

>       Close friends

# Danger Zone

We learned that our comfort zone helps us feel safe and in control of ourselves.

When we are in our comfort zone, we can manage our behaviors and emotions.

When we feel out of control and ready to blow up, we have landed in the Danger Zone.

There are lots of ways to recognize danger in our day-to-day activities. Here is a short list of things that signal danger.

- Signs that say Warning! or Danger!
- Sirens
- Alarms
- Flashing lights

Can you name other things that signal danger?

_____          _____

_____          _____

_____          _____

_____          _____

_____          _____

There are certain feelings that make us feel out of control, and we each have our own ideas about which feelings lead us to the Danger Zone. For example, some people can just laugh when they are teased about something, but other people get very angry when they feel teased by someone. This makes them feel out of control. Anger about being teased may lead that person to the Danger Zone.

Look through the situations listed, and circle any that could be a Danger Zone for you.

Feeling ignored                    Feeling misunderstood

Feeling leftout                    Feeling teased or pickedon by others

Feeling overwhelmed                Feeling tired

List other situations that are a Danger Zone for you.

_____

_____

_____

_____

_____

We may not always be able to avoid our Danger Zone, but we can try to be prepared.

# Danger Zone

## Plan Ahead and Be Prepared

Ask a helpful adult to do this activity with you.

Pick 1 of the circled Danger Zones from the previous page or one you listed.

Imagine yourself in this Danger Zone and tell a story about it. Give as many details as possible about how the situation started and how you felt.

_____

_____

_____

_____

_____

_____

_____

_____

_____

_____

_____

_____

_____

_____

_____

_____

_____

_____

_____

# Activity 37

Now let's find 3 different ways for the story to end so that you are using self-control and staying calm. You and the adult will come up with several different ideas that would help if you landed in the Danger Zone.

List your endings here.

1._____

_____

_____

_____

_____


2._____

_____

_____

_____

_____


3._____

_____

_____

_____

_____


Repeat this activity for other Danger Zones you listed.

Emotional Danger Zones aren't a problem when we are prepared!

# Will This Fly?

Part of solving problems is testing different ideas to see if they work.

The testing process is called trial and error. This means once an idea is formed it is tried to see how well it works. Sometimes, when someone has a new idea, people will ask, "Will this fly?"

Rarely do things go just right on the first try. Changes can be made after the "trial" (after the idea is tried), and then it is tried again with the changes. This process continues until we decide whether this is a good idea or not.

Often people avoid trial and error because of the "error" part.

It can be frustrating when an idea doesn't work as we hoped it would. When we have the blues, we may give up on an idea before the trial and error, to avoid feeling frustration.

Think about what it is like to feel frustrated. Let's identify a few frustrating situations.

- My teacher is angry because I forgot to turn in homework 2 days in a row.
- Mom said she would pick up my favorite snack, but she got busy and forgot.
- My friend was going to call me after school, but I wasn't home to get the call.

It is expected that we will feel frustrated in these situations. When we feel frustrated, it is an opportunity to solve a problem. This is when we need to use trial-and-error thinking to help us find a solution to the problem. Here are some trial solutions to the frustrating situations listed above.

- Make a colorful note to include late homework with other homework tomorrow.
- Remind mom about the snacks, and put the empty snack jar out on the counter.
- Call my friend and tell him I'm sorry I missed his call because I wanted to talk.

Each of these is a good idea for dealing with the frustrations, but we won't know how they work until we try them.

Here is a great way to practice solving problems with trial and error.

Make a paper airplane from any piece of paper.

If you have never made a paper airplane, find someone who knows how to show you the way it is done.

Will this fly?

After you have made the paper airplane, find a safe room or go outdoors to test the plane.

Try several different flying techniques, and see what works best.

Now make changes to the paper airplane by adding something or taking something away.

For example, try adding glue, tape, or string to the airplane.

Does this make the plane fly better or not?

You may even add glitter, sequins, or feathers.

Perhaps you want to cut flaps on the wings or put tape on the nose.

Try lots of different ideas and ask yourself, "Will this fly?"

Make several different planes, and try different methods of folding. Which combinations work the best for you?

The next time you feel frustrated, come up with a trial solution and ask yourself,

"Will this fly?"

# All in the Family

Our families are an important part of our lives. Each family is unique and has special qualities. Let's think about your family and what makes it special.

In the space below, create a family portrait using a pencil, pen, or markers.

Write the names of everyone in your family in the space below.

_____          _____

_____          _____

_____          _____

_____          _____

_____          _____

Do you know their ages?  If you do, write the ages next to their names.

# All in the Family

Do you have any family pets? Write the pet's name in the space with the family names.

Pick a color for each member of your family.

Use that color to make a circle around the names of the females and a square around the names of the males.

Use different lines to show the connections between the family members.

Make a strong straight line to the people in your family with whom you talk about your feelings.

Make a squiggly or loopy line to the people in your family who are hard to talk to about your feelings.

Make a dotted or broken line to the people whom you do not talk to about your feelings.

Make any other connections that you would like to the family names.

Make a large circle around all the family members, and color it any way you like.

We have looked at your family connections and identified the family members you can talk to about your feelings.

When you have the blues, remember these connections and share your feelings with those people.

If you need help with talking about your feelings, try any of these activities:

|  |  |  |  |
|---|---|---|---|
| Activity 24 | Open Mike | Activity 33 | Hey, Listen Up! |
| Activity 19 | My Move | Activity 34 | My Favorites |

The people who care about you want to help, but they can't know your true feelings if you keep them to yourself.

Share your thoughts and feelings with others to feel better and beat the blues!

Animals are interesting and fun to watch. They have many skills and abilities that help them survive in the wild.

Think of all the animals in the world. Pick one animal that you admire and would use as a way to describe yourself.

List all the skills and abilities of this animal. For example, is the animal a fast runner, a good swimmer, friendly, strong?

Animal traits      _____     _____

                         _____     _____

                         _____     _____

What do you like best about this animal?

_____

What is the animal's greatest strength?

_____

What does the animal use for protection when in danger?

_____

Use the mask form on the next page to create an animal mask.

Be creative by adding color, stripes, dots, or feathers.

What skills and abilities does your animal have that you would like to have?

Imagine you have the same strengths and abilities as your animal.

You may make a photocopy the mask and attach string or a stick so you can wear it while playing.

This activity is great for the whole family. Ask each person in the family to participate.

Imagine you see a person smiling and laughing.

What might they be feeling? _____

_____

_____

_____

_____

_____

_____

Draw the face of a person smiling and laughing.

Imagine you see a person frowning and crying.

What might they be feeling? _____

_____

_____

_____

_____

_____

_____

Draw the face of a person frowning and crying.

# Many Faces, Many Feelings

Imagine you see a person listening to a good story.

What might they be feeling? _____

_____

_____

_____

_____

_____

_____

Draw the face of a person listening to a good story.

Imagine you see a person who is ready to eat lunch.

What might they be feeling? _____

_____

_____

_____

_____

_____

_____

Draw a face of a person who is ready to eat lunch.

# Activity 41

## Many Faces, Many Feelings

Look at your face in a mirror.

What are you feeling?_____

_____

_____

_____

_____

_____

Draw your face showing this feeling.

# Many Faces, Many Feelings

Activity 41

Look again at the drawings you did, and imagine other feelings that could be associated with these faces.

Give each face 2 other feeling words to describe the faces.
For example, for the first face that is laughing and smiling you may have said they were feeling happy. Other feeling words for this face could be excited, hopeful, or cheerful.

This activity reminds us that for the many faces we see there are many feelings.

Often we think we know how someone feels by looking at them, and we may think others should know our feelings from our facial expressions. Be helpful, and let others know your feelings.

Remembering the good things we have experienced can help us through bad times.

This activity will show how we feel grateful and fortunate to have family, friends, and good times.

# My Highlights

Good times and great memories can be listed here.

The best time I ever had was _____

My best friends are   _____   _____

_____   _____

Adults I really like are _____   _____

_____   _____

The best thing about school is _____

The best thing about my family is _____

Other special highlights are

_____   _____

_____   _____

Use your highlights to fill in the spaces on the Wheel of Fortune on the next page.

First, put your name in the center circle.

For each space on the wheel, put the name of a good friends and adults you really like. Also include activities or memories of times when you were enjoying yourself.

Use pens, markers, or crayons to color your Wheel of Fortune any way you like.

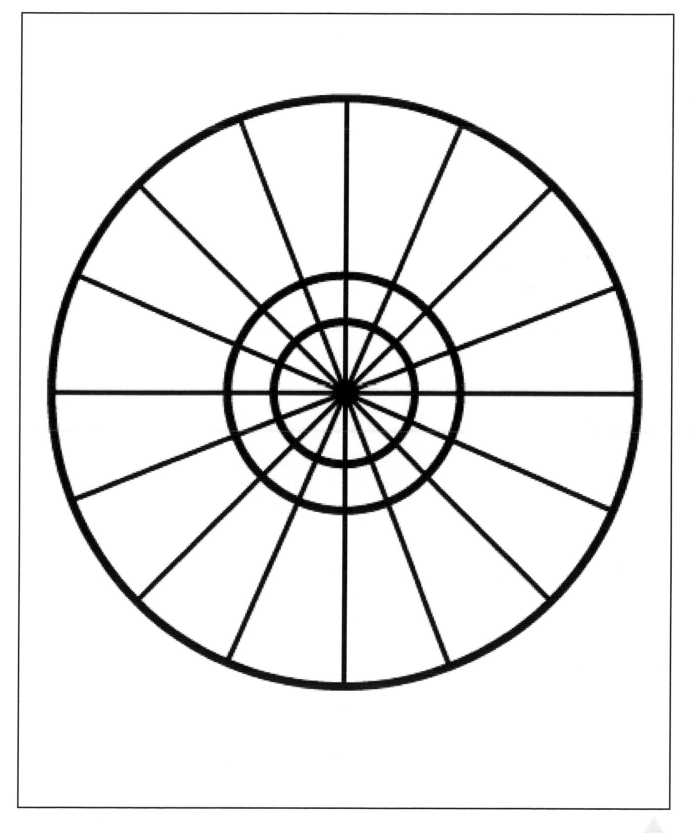

When we have the blues, there are some days that look dreary and grey.

Move the grey away, and create a world of color!

In the space below, draw a world of your own.  Be creative and use your own personal style in this drawing. If you have art materials, use a large sheet of paper for this drawing. Add lots of color to the drawing using markers, colored pencils, or gel pens.

# A World of Color

**Color Your World**

What is your favorite color? Write your name with this color in the space below.

_____

Did you use this color in your drawing?

Write 3 feeling words you associate with this color.

_____

_____

_____

Pick 2 other colors from your drawing and write 3 feeling words for those colors.

Color: _____     Color: _____

Feelings:_____     Feelings:_____

_____        _____

_____        _____

Be sure to notice all the colors around you each day. Look for your favorite colors as you play and point them out to others.

Enjoy your world of color!

Take a moment to think about your hopes and dreams.

Use your imagination to picture yourself as you always hoped you would be.

Hold this thought, and picture yourself around your family and friends.

Next, picture yourself doing something that you really enjoy.

Color the Dream Chair any way you would like.

If you have clay, play dough, or other art materials, create your own Dream Chair.

Keep the Dream Chair around to inspire you to reach for your dreams!

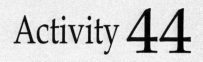
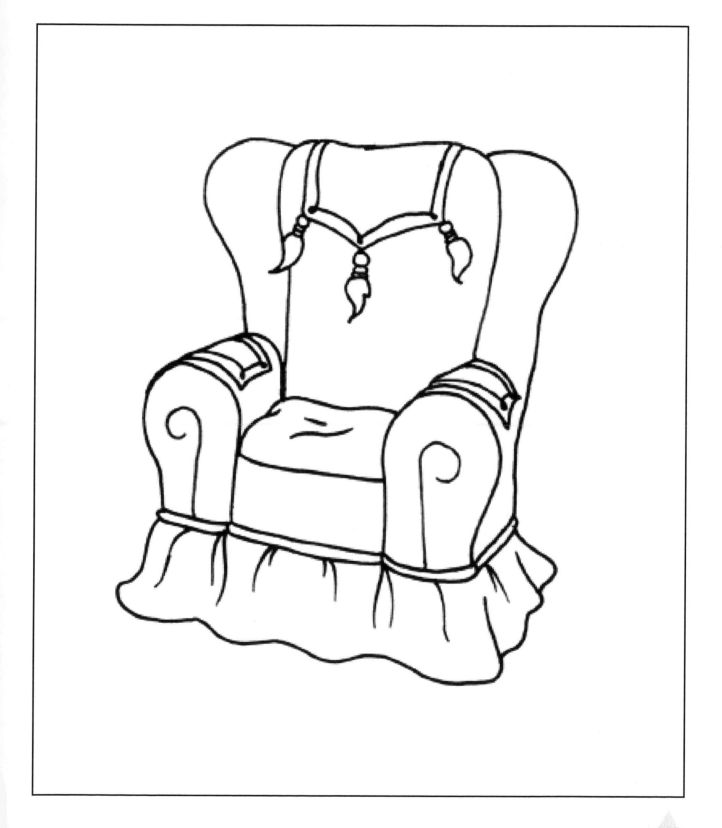

# Notes

# Notes

# Notes